Fun with your Doll

Hairstyles, Crafts & More!

★ American Girl®

Craft with Care!

When making crafts for dolls, be aware that dyes from ribbons, felt, beads, and other supplies may bleed or rub off onto a doll and leave permanent stains. To help prevent this, use light colors when possible, and check your doll often to make sure colors aren't transferring to her body or vinyl. And never get your doll wet! Water greatly increases the risk of dye rub-off.

When you see this symbol, always ask an adult to help you.

Published by American Girl Publishing, Inc.
Copyright © 2008 by American Girl, LLC

All rights reserved. No part of this book may be used or reproduced in any manner whatsoever without written permission.

Questions or comments? Call 1-800-845-0005,
visit our Web site at **americangirl.com**,
or write to Customer Service, American Girl, 8400 Fairway Place, Middleton, WI 53562-0497.

Printed in China

09 10 11 12 13 14 15 LEO 15 14 13 12 11 10 9

All American Girl marks are trademarks of American Girl, LLC.

Editorial Development: Trula Magruder; Art Direction & Design: Camela Decaire; Craft Styling: Carrie Anton; Production: Jeannette Bailey, Gretchen Krause, Judith Lary, Paula Moon Bailey; Photography: Radlund Studios; Styling: Carrie Anton, Mandy Crary

Dear Reader,

Inside this book, you'll discover dozens of ways you and your doll can spend your days together. Throw parties, design accessories, play games—before you know it, you'll have a friendship like no other. Start with a fun idea, end with a good-night kiss, and create many happy memories in the middle.

Your friends at American Girl

Find a Name

The first gift you give your doll will be her name, so make it a special one.

- Think of a name you'll love saying over and over.
- Name your doll after someone special.
- Choose a name with a beautiful meaning. (Check out our list for some ideas.)

Aisha—alive

Alexis—helper

Amanda—lovable

Amber—jewel

Amika—friendly

Amy—beloved

Andrea—brave

Angelina—little angel

Anoush—sweet

Bailey—helpful

Bambi—young girl

Bella—beautiful

Bonnie— pretty

Briana—strong

Cailin —girl

Cara—dear

Caroline—melody, strong

Cher—darling

Dakota—friend

Delilah—delicate

Emily—hardworking

Emma—welcoming

Erin—peace

Farah—joy

Gabrielle—angel

Hannah—gracious

Hilary—cheerful

Jasmine—flower

Jessica—gift

Julia—youthful

Katie—pure

Kimberly—ruler

Megan—strong

Miranda—miracle

Morgan—from the sea

Natalie—born on Christmas

Novia—girlfriend

Paige—young

Regina—queen

Ruth—friend

Sage or Sophia—wise

Sarah—princess

Shannon—small, wise

Sierra—nature's beauty

Winona—first-born daughter

Zoe—life

Decorate Her Space

Define your doll's corner of the room with playful posters.

Cut out magazine pictures and hang them on the wall to make posters for your doll. Check with a parent before you tape or pin up the posters.

Make Jewelry

Design matching necklaces to celebrate
your great friendship.

String matching paper cutouts, stickers, letter beads,
or photos onto light-colored cords, ribbons, or chains.
Make a large necklace for yourself and a small one for
your doll.

Create a Style that Shines

Your doll will shimmer with glittering hair accessories.

Glue a sparkly pom-pom to a mini claw clip, a jewel to a snap clip, or glitter to a small barrette. Let dry completely before styling your doll's hair. To style, pull a small section of hair up on one side and clip in place.

Serve Snacks

Pass out perfect-sized treats for two.

Invite friends and their dolls to your place and serve regular-sized and mini-sized sweet and salty snacks.

Hang Photos

Build a photo gallery of close friends for your doll—without snapping a picture!

Cut out doll and pet photos from catalogues, and tape them to small squares of card stock. Tape or glue the photos to ribbon strips. Ask a parent if it's O.K. to hang the ribbons on the wall near your doll's bed.

Serve Breakfast

Your doll will flip over these homemade pancakes!

Color 1¾-inch round, flat wood pieces with crayons. Cut yellow craft foam into butter pats and place the pats on the pretend pancakes. Serve on a tiny plate or cut a plate from a cupcake liner.

Accent a Band with Bows

Hold back your doll's hair with a bunch of bitty bows.

Tie light-colored ribbon scraps onto a small section of a hair elastic. Trim the ribbons short to look like little bows. Slip the elastic on your doll's hair so that the bows rest on top of her head.

Play a Game

Two can play this game—especially when you make up the rules!

Cut a 5-by-5-inch piece of black craft foam. Glue a slightly smaller piece of white paper to the foam. Cut or punch out tiny colored-paper squares, and glue them into a path for spaces. Stick a large circle at the start and the finish of the path. Use buttons, beads, and foam for playing pieces.

Take a Family Photo

Pose for a picture you'll both treasure.

Ask someone to take a photo of you and your doll in a cute pose. Slip the picture into a sweet paper frame and give it to your doll.

Go to Gymnastics

Practice makes perfect!

Lay a board on top of two book stacks and help your doll create a balance-beam routine. Add music to the routine before showing it to friends and family.

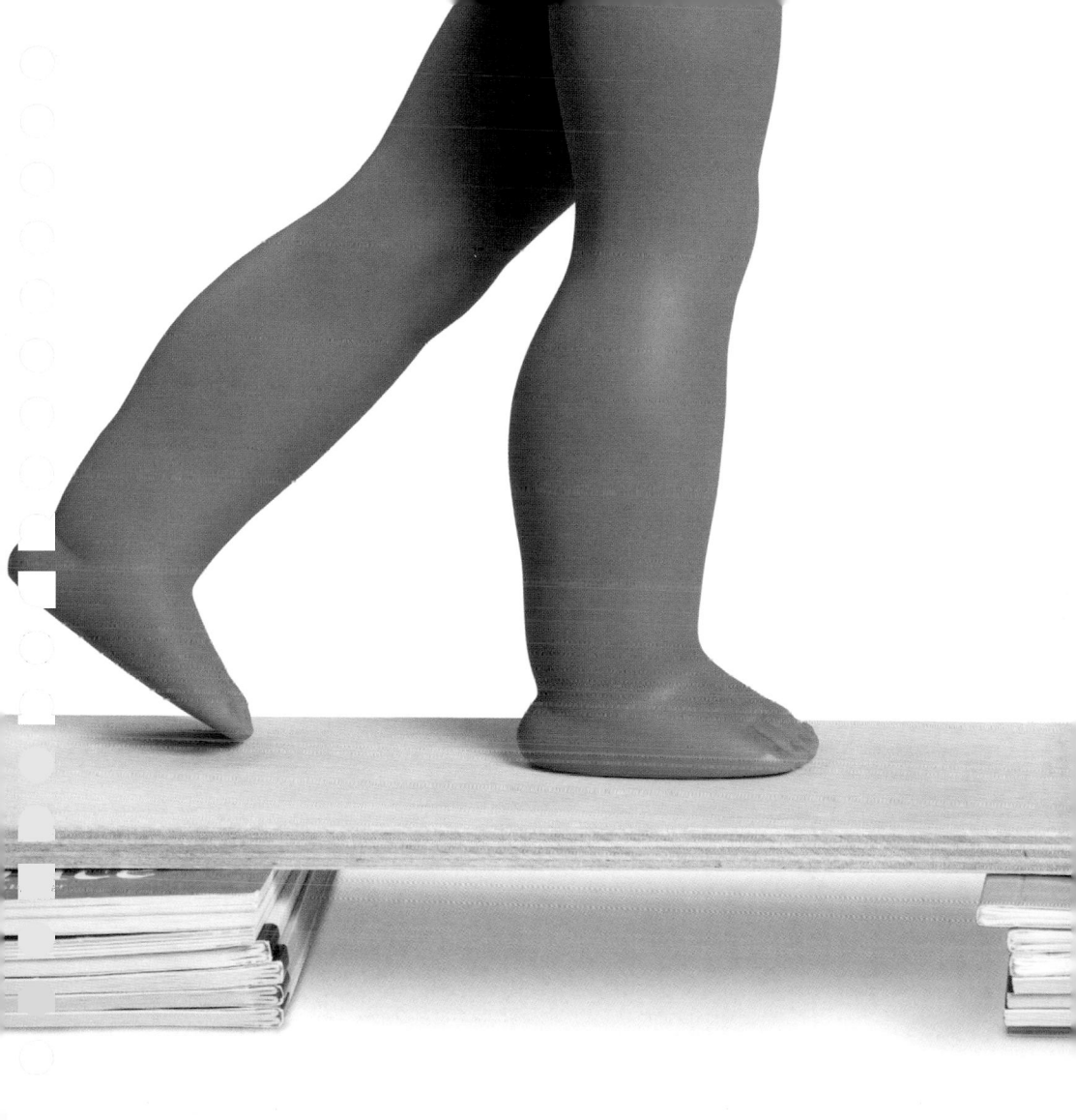

Make a Headband

Your doll can be a trendsetter with this one-of-a-kind hair accessory.

Sort through light-colored sewing trims and ribbon scraps to find the perfect headband for your doll's hair or outfit. If your doll's hair is thick, opt for a wide band so that it'll stand out. Tie the band under your doll's hair in back.

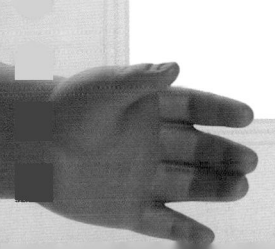

Open a Café

Treat your doll to dinner out.

Before opening a dinky diner, make a menu. Cut the edges of a playing card with craft scissors for a place mat. Trim a cupcake liner for a plate. Cut the corner off a paper napkin, fold it, and tie it closed with string. Cut the bottom off a cupcake liner and tape the liner sides around a marker cap for a vase. Drop in a mini flower. Finally, take your doll's order, and serve her dinner—just don't expect a "big" tip!

Play Outside

Get your doll moving with these popular outdoor games.

With a colored pencil or chalk, draw a hopscotch board onto construction paper. Use a tiny pebble for the rock. Place a sticker onto a plastic lid to make a doll-sized Frisbee. For rubber balls, decorate Ping-Pong balls with markers. Let dry.

Give First Aid

Get supplies ready for small accidents.

If your doll takes a fall, you'll be ready with a first-aid kit. Buy a ready-made kit for dolls or gather supplies, such as white cloth strips, to wrap up your doll's ankle, arm, or wrist. For a cast, wrap the cloth between her thumb and fingers and tape the end in place—and then add cute stickers!

Get Well

Cheer up your sick friend with these get-well essentials.

Fold a small paper rectangle in half, and add a sticker to the front for a get-well card. For a flower, draw two circles on tissue paper. Cut out the circles with craft scissors, and stack them. Gather the paper in the center, and have an adult help you wrap a chenille stem around the gather. Make a second flower. Slip a brown pom-pom into a tiny pot, and "plant" the flowers.

Tie on a Towel

Your doll will stand out in the crowd
with a bitty beach towel.

For the perfect beach towel, choose a light-colored
dish towel or a large washcloth. Wrap the towel
around your doll's body and tuck in the corners. Use a
mini claw clip to help hold the towel in place.

Sparkle at a Special Event

Add a bit of glitz to your doll's wardrobe.

Your doll will shimmer at any occasion if you tie a light-colored sparkly ribbon around the waist of her party dress.

Build a Campfire

Gather around a flickering fire.

"Roast" marshmallows over a pretend fire at your next campout. To make the fire, cut flames from orange and yellow tissue paper. Twist the flame ends together, and glue them between cinnamon-stick logs. Slip mini marshmallows onto sticks.

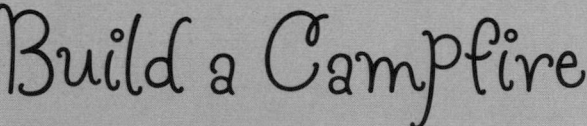

Style a Sweet 'Do

Try this adorable hairstyle if your doll has long hair.

Make a small braid on each side of your doll's face. Pull the braids together in back, and hold them together with an elastic band. Slip on a fancy barrette to hide the elastic.

Decorate a Cake

Make your doll's birthday the best ever.

Cover a small, round cardboard box with white paper. Glue on white yarn for icing trims. Add dots and other decorations. For a candle, poke a paper flame into a small piece of mini straw, and then slip the straw inside a bead. Glue the candle to the cake. Now don't forget to sing!

Crown the Birthday Girl

Design a tiara for your doll's birthday.

Ask an adult to help you slip shank buttons onto a chenille stem. Slip the chenille stem ends into your doll's hair. Bend the ends of the chenille stems around your doll's hair to keep the crown in place.

Paint a Portrait

Capture a special moment in your doll's life by painting her picture.

Pull out your paintbrushes, markers, crayons, or chalks, and create a portrait of your doll. Frame the artwork and hang it up or place it on your desk as a memento of your friendship.

Presenting

Bella's Fashion Show!

When: 7 p.m.

Where: Bella's bedroom

Doll Models: Tina & Kelly

Stage a Fashion Show

Parade your doll's latest fashions.

Set up a doll fashion show. Make a sign to advertise the event. Invite your best friends over with their dolls, and mix and match clothes to create new outfits. Lead the dolls down the runway.

Start a Band

Turn your doll into the latest rock-and-roll sensation.

Make your doll the lead singer in her own band. Dress her like a star—including a cool hairstyle. And give her a microphone. To make a mic, cover half a crayon with aluminum foil. Glue a pom-pom on top. Fill the seats with fans and start the show!

Take Skating Lessons

Show your doll how to spin
on her new ice pond.

Cut a sheet of aluminum foil into a pond shape. Slip
ice skates on your doll or tape construction-paper
blades to her shoe bottoms. Show her how to do
figure eights on the ice.

Make Cocoa

Tiny fingers stay toasty warm when they hold a cup of hot chocolate.

Slip a brown pom-pom into a doll's cup for cocoa.
Add tiny white pom-poms for marshmallows.
Mmmm.

Create a Comfy Cap

Keep your doll's head cozy in this winter hat.

Lose a glove? Cut off the fingertips of the remaining light-colored glove to make a cap. Slip the glove over your doll's head, and tie the fingers together with yarn.

Bake Cookies

When the temperature drops, heat things up with these cute cookies!

Cut craft foam into your favorite cookies. Glue on the chips and layers. For a platter, punch two holes on each side of a paper plate. Slip a light-colored ribbon through the holes on each side to make a loop, and then glue the ribbon ends underneath the plate.

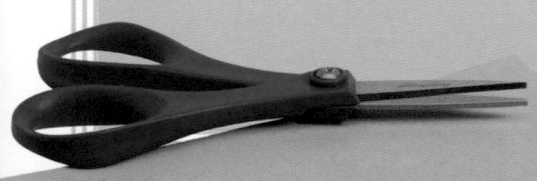

Say Good Night

Create a routine to help your
doll fall asleep.

If your doll's having trouble getting to sleep, dress her
in her softest pj's, tuck her into bed, tell her a bedtime
story (not a scary one!), and then kiss her good night.

Design a Wallet

Your doll can carry her cards
in this pretty wallet.

Cut out a 3-by-6-inch piece of felt. Fold the long end up 2½ inches to make a pocket, leaving a 1-inch flap. Glue the two sides together. With an adult's help, sew a button on the top of the pocket. Fold the flap down and cut a small slit in the felt right over the button. Slip the button through the slit to close. Punch out the cards on the following pages, and slip a few of them into the wallet.

Travel Pass

Jewelry Cleaners Pet Store

valid for one month

Gift Card

So Small Shop

$25   4832 65 2238 00

Public Library

Central, East, Downtown,
Northwest & Ridgeway Branches

signature here

★ American Girl®

C A F E

Enjoy the show!

Enjoy the show!

Enjoy the show!

AMERICAN GIRL
DANCE ACADEMY

This is to certify that

....

*has completed the
American Girl Babysitter's
Training Course
and has the skills and knowledge
to care for young children.*

Instructor: *Ms. Liang*

Good Sport Award

This is to certify that

....

has demonstrated outstanding
sportsmanship this season.

Awarded by: *Coach Potter*

Lunch Menu

Warm Welcome
Cinnamon Buns

First Course
Fresh Fruit Kabobs

Entrée Selections
Cilantro-Lime Chicken Salad
Rosemary Chicken Sandwich
American Girl Picnic Lunch
Tic-Tac-Toe Pizza

Sweet Surprises
Chocolate Mousse Flowerpot
with an individual cake and a
seasonal sugar cookie

Courtesy of the
**Greater Metropolitan
Transit Service**

For fare and rate information, call
1-800-555-5555.

So Small Shop

For balance inquiry, call
1-800-555-5555.

This prepaid gift card is redeemable for merchandise anywhere in the United States within
24 months of purchase. It is void after 2 years and is not redeemable for cash.

The person whose signature appears on the
front of this card is responsible for all materials
borrowed using this card.

**Member of the
Public Library System**

Ballet Certificate

This certifies that

_____

has completed the

American Girl Dance Academy

course in ballet.

Instructor: *Madame Saylor*

Movie Ticket	Admit One 6:00 PM Double Feature	Movie Ticket
Movie Ticket	Admit One 6:00 PM Double Feature	Movie Ticket
Movie Ticket	Free Popcorn & 16-ounce Soda	Movie Ticket

American Girl
Babysitting
Training

Graduation Certificate

My Doll's Profile

My doll's name:

Her birthday:

My doll's best friends:

My doll's favorite outfit:

What I like best about my doll:

Things we like to do together:

_____

_____

Our best adventure so far:

_____

_____

Our favorite activity in this book:

_____

_____